GHOST'S JOURNEY:

A Refugee Story

by Robin Stevenson

Illustrations created from
photographs by Rainer Oktovianus

Ghost lived in a small
apartment on the
beautiful island of Java,
with her two dads.

When Rainer played video games,
Ghost snuggled by the headphones and purred.

When Eka cooked gulai, Ghost stood on her back legs and begged for a taste.

When friends
came over,
Ghost played
with everyone.

But when strangers came to the door,
Rainer and Eka turned off the lights and
pretended no one was home.

Ghost wanted to help.

She fetched them toys to play with.

She snuggled close and licked their tears. "People don't like us, Ghost," Rainer whispered, "just because Eka and I love each other."

Over and over, they had to move. Ghost did not like moving.

She hid behind the curtains,

and on top of book shelves where she felt safe.

She hid beneath the bed, inside a paper bag.

Over and over, Rainer said, "Sorry, Ghost.

It isn't safe for us here."

Ghost knew they couldn't keep hiding.

If her dads were in danger, she would be a guard cat.

Ghost listened for footsteps in the hallway.

She kept
watch at
the window.

MEOW!!

One rainy day, Ghost spotted
people in uniforms far down below.
She meowed and meowed until
her dads looked outside too.
"Police!" Rainer said.

The next thing Ghost knew, she was being scooped up and pushed into a bag.

Rainer and Eka
ran with her —

bump

bump

bump

down the fire
escape stairs
and all the way
across town.

Ghost
flattened
her ears
and
yowled!

When the police
were gone, Rainer
and Eka took Ghost
back home.

But Ghost did not
feel safe.

Rainer and Eka sat at the computer. Click, click, click went their fingers.

"Maybe someone can help us," Rainer told Ghost. "Maybe we can find a place where we won't have to hide."

Ghost lay down on the keyboard and purred
so that they wouldn't forget about her.

Many long months went by. Then, one afternoon,
Ghost's dads danced into the room.

"We're leaving, Ghost!" Rainer said.

"I have our plane tickets!" Eka waved papers in the air.

They hugged each other and twirled around the room together. Ghost twirled too, weaving in and out of their legs. "This is the happiest day of our lives," Rainer said. "In Canada, we will be free."

A few days later, it was time to go.

"You'll be safe in here," Eka said.

A cage? No way! thought Ghost.

"I'm sorry, Ghost." Rainer closed the door behind her. Ghost yowled in protest as they carried her out of the apartment.

She wailed when they arrived in a strange place where people stood in long lines.

She yowled and she wailed until she was thirsty and exhausted. Finally, she fell asleep.

When she woke up, she pushed her face
up against the bars. Where was she now?
"Don't worry," Eka said. "We're right here."
But all Ghost could see was their feet.

She was stuck in the cage for hours . . .
and hours . . . and hours. Sometimes she slept.
Sometimes she meowed so her dads wouldn't
forget about her.

Ghost felt a bump and a screech.

She heard people clapping.

"This is your pilot speaking," said a voice.

"Welcome to Vancouver!"

Outside the sky was grey. It smelled different.

Rain was falling and the air was soft and clean.

A short ride in a taxi . . . and then they arrived.

"No more moves, Ghost." Eka opened her cage door.

"This is our home now."

It was so cold in this new country! Ghost buried herself in a pile of blankets.

But soon she grew curious. She peeked out the window and saw seagulls flying. She made a chirping sound, like a bird, and her dads laughed.

Now, Ghost
lives in her new
apartment with
her two dads.

When Rainer
plays video
games,
Ghost curls
on his lap
and purrs.

When Eka
goes for walks
in the snow,
Ghost loves
to go with him.

At night, Ghost sleeps on her dads' bed,
like she has since she was a kitten.

. . . And they never,
ever have to hide.

~ The End ~

In the summer of 2016, Rainer and Eka attended their first Pride parade in Canada.

Ghost stayed home to take a nap.

Author's Note: This picture book is based on a true story.

In more than 70 countries around the world, same-sex relationships are criminalized. One of those countries is Indonesia—the country where Ghost's dads, Eka Nasution and Rainer Oktovianus, were born and grew up. In 2010, they met and fell in love. Only their closest friends knew about their relationship. But both men spoke up publicly for LGBTQ+ rights and soon they began receiving threats.

They had to move at least seven times, but the threats continued. They couldn't turn to the police—in Indonesia, the police were hostile and often abusive toward LGBTQ+ people.

So, fearing for their lives, they reached out to a Canadian organization called Rainbow Railroad which helps LGBTQ+ people around the world escape from danger. After getting helpful information and advice, they made a plan. Rainer applied for a visa to study in Canada and Eka applied for a work visa.

They sold their belongings and saved as much money as they could. And when their visas finally arrived, they boarded a flight to Canada. Their cat, Ghost, travelled with them. They had rescued her from an abandoned chicken coop when she was only a few weeks old. Rainer and Eka had to leave almost everything behind when they left Indonesia, but they couldn't bear to leave Ghost.

The couple found an apartment in Vancouver, BC. While some people come to Canada as refugees, Rainer and Eka applied for refugee status soon after they arrived, from inside the country. A Vancouver-based community group called Rainbow Refugee supported them at their hearing. Their application was successful and they were granted refugee status. In 2018, they became permanent residents of Canada. Rainer is a photographer; Eka works in healthcare. They talk about possibly adopting a child someday. For now, they enjoy spending time at home together—with Ghost, of course! Rainer and Eka volunteer with Rainbow Refugee and Foundation of Hope to support other LGBTQ+ refugees from all over the world.

All of the author's royalties from the sale of this book will be donated to support LGBTQ+ refugees through Rainbow Refugee and Rainbow Railroad, and through Canada's Private Sponsorship of Refugees (PSR) program. The publisher, Rebel Mountain Press, will also donate partial proceeds from the sale of this book to those same organizations. Rainer and Eka will be donating their share of the proceeds to help animals find new homes in Canada.

ABOUT THE AUTHOR

Robin Stevenson is an award-winning author of more than 20 books for kids and teens, including the Stonewall Honor book PRIDE: CELEBRATING DIVERSITY AND COMMUNITY and the board book PRIDE COLORS. Her writing has been translated into a number of languages and published in more than ten countries. Her books have been nominated for many awards, including the Governor General's Literary Award, and she is a four-time finalist for the BC Book Prizes. Robin lives with her family on Vancouver Island and has been involved with refugee sponsorship since 2015. You can find her online: www.robinstevenson.com

Special Thanks:

Thank you to Marilyn MacPherson, Librarian, for the idea of turning the story of Rainer, Eka, and their cat, Ghost, into this picture book. (Original story published in *Breaking Boundaries: LGBTQ2 Writers on Coming Out and Into Canada* by Rebel Mountain Press, 2017.)

Reviews

"Stevenson tells the real-life story of Eka Nasution and Rainer Oktovianus with simplicity and clarity for a younger audience. Both the primary text and the author's note are written in accessible language, and centering Ghost creates appeal for young readers, who can easily identify with her family's longing to live their true lives. This introduction to LGBTQ human rights for young children is a gentle and effective one." ~ Kirkus Reviews

"The world is changing, and Canada remains, at least in comparison to the global landscape, an LGBTQ safe space, and Ghost's Journey plays a role in reinforcing this narrative for a positive purpose. If only more LGBTQ refugees had a Ghost to keep them company through the immigration process!"
"Highly Recommended" ~ Canadian Review of Materials

What educators and librarians have to say about *Ghost's Journey*

"Ghost's Journey is a perfect fit for teaching young audiences about SOGI, family diversity, human rights and social justice. Parents, primary teachers, and elementary school librarians will love this picture book; a 'must have' on every kid's bookshelf!"
~Solveig Davie, Teacher-Librarian, SD44 (North Vancouver, BC)

"Heartwarming and powerful story of courage, a cat's love, and a new country. Inspirational."
~ Marilyn MacPherson, Librarian

"With gentle, evocative prose, and a cuddly protagonist, Stevenson recounts Eka and Rainer's journey from Java through the lens of the two men's cat, Ghost. Ghost's perspective provides young readers with an accessible entry point to explore the plight of LGBTQ immigrants fleeing violence in their own countries. Ghost's Journey is hopeful and engaging, packing an emotional punch that will help illuminate the struggles of LGBTQ individuals at home and abroad."
~Robert Bittner, LGBTQ Literature Scholar, MA Children's Literature program, UBC

Published by Rebel Mountain Press, 2019

Text copyright © 2019 by Robin Stevenson

Photographs copyright © 2019 by Rainer Oktovianus and Rebel Mountain Press
(Note: the illustrations were digitally rendered from Rainer's photographs using Photoshop software
— resulting illustrated images by Rebel Mountain Press)
Ghost thinks she looks quite attractive in all of the illustrations.

Library and Archives Canada Cataloguing in Publication

Title: Ghost's journey : a refugee story / author, Robin Stevenson ; photographer, Rainer
Oktovianus.
Other titles: Refugee story
Names: Stevenson, Robin, 1968- author. | Oktovianus, Rainer, 1983- photographer.
Identifiers: Canadiana 20189068973 | ISBN 9781775301943 (hardcover)
Classification: LCC PS8637.T487 G56 2019 | DDC jC813/.6—dc23

All interior and cover photo credits courtesy of Rainer Oktovianus
except for pp: 2, 11, 14-17, 22, 24 photos by Pixabay.com & pp 19, 26-7 by Pxhere.com
and rendered digitally into illustrations by Rebel Mountain Press.

Printed and bound in Canada by Friesens
Issued in hardcover format:
ISBN 978-1-7753019-4-3 (bound)
Rebel Mountain Press—Nanoose Bay, BC, Canada
We acknowledge that we are located on the traditional territory of the Snaw-Na-Was First Nation

www.rebelmountainpress.com

1 2 3 4 5 6 7 8 9 10